For my n
with mu
- Christmas '2

THE *Mother's* BOOK

ELMA VAN VLIET

Dedication

....

....

....

....

....

CONTENTS

HUMAN AFFECTION

Mother I love you so.
Said the child, I love you more than I know.
She laid her head on her mother's arm,
And the love between them kept them warm.

Stevie Smith

Every life knows its difficult moments. One of mine was on October 23rd, 2001, when the doctors in the hospital told me that my mother didn't have much longer to live. On my way back home and during the weeks that followed, I spent a lot of time trying to handle the prospect of my mother dying. It was an emotional time, filled with feelings of sadness, anger and despair.

The hardest part was thinking about how my future would be – a future without my Mum. She wouldn't be there at the important moments in my life. She would never see her grandchildren grow up, never see me in my wedding dress. But, even more devastating, I would never be able to ask her all the things I still had left to ask. I still had so many questions, and I still wanted to know so much – about her, about me and about how she had felt at particular moments in her life.

This is why I created *The Mother's Book*. I realised the truth in the saying: "You don't know what you have, until it's gone". And I realised how precious time is and how little of it we dedicate to the people who matter most. People like mothers.

I hope that, while writing, you will connect and share. That *The Mother's Book* will not only bring happiness as you discover little things you never knew about each other, but will also create new bonds between you, as you bring back memories long-forgotten.

How old are you as you fill this in:

How old am I as you fill this in:

WHEN YOU WERE LITTLE

When and where were you born?

Did your birth take place at home or in a hospital?

What was happening in the world at the moment you were born?

What kind of child were you when you were small?

Was there a special story or rhyme that your mother always read or sang to you at bed time? Do you still remember the words?

Here's room for some pictures of you when you were small

What was your favourite book and why were you so fond of it?

What is your favourite book now?

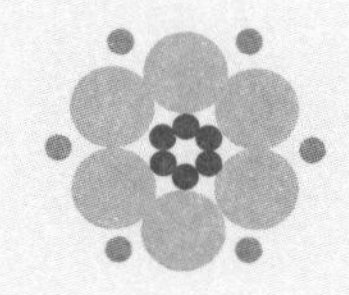

It was the lock of the door which had been closed ten years, and she put her hand in her pocket, drew out the key, and found it fitted the keyhole. She put the key in and turned it. It took two hands to do it, and it did turn.

And then she took a long breath and looked behind her up the long walk to see if anyone was coming. No one was coming. No one ever did come, it seemed, and she took another long breath, because she could not help it, and she held back the swinging curtain of ivy and pushed back the door which opened slowly – slowly.

Then she slipped through it, and shut it behind her, and stood with her back against it, looking about her and breathing quite fast with excitement, and wonder, and delight.

She was standing inside the secret garden.

THE SECRET GARDEN

Frances Hodgson Burnett

What is one of your favourite childhood memories?

TELL ME ABOUT ME

What kind of child was I when I was little? Did I resemble you or my father, or did I have my own distinctive character?

Here's room for some pictures of me when I was small

Was there a special story or rhyme you always read or sang to me before I fell asleep? Do you still remember the words?

YOUR PARENTS

What kind of parents did you have? Were they progressive or old-fashioned?

What kind of jobs did your parents have?

Can you draw our family tree (it doesn't matter if you can't do it perfectly!)

She was my first, great love. She was a wonderful, rare woman – you do not know; as strong, and steadfast, and generous as the sun. She could be as swift as a white whiplash, and as kind and gentle as warm rain, and as steadfast as the irreducible earth beneath us.

D H Lawrence

Which of your parents do you resemble most physically? How can you tell?

What are the fondest memories you have of your father?

What are the most precious memories you have of your mother?

What are the most important lessons about life your parents gave you?

Which characteristics of my grandparents do you recognise in me?

Here's some space for photographs of your parents

A CHILD'S EVENING PRAYER

Ere on my bed my limbs I lay,
God grant me peace my prayers to say;
O God! Preserve my mother dear
In strength and health for many a year;
And, O! preserve my father too,
And may I pay him reverence due;
And may I my best thoughts employ
To be my parents' hope and joy;
And O! preserve my brother's both
From evil doings and from sloth,
And may we always love each other,
Our friends, our father, and our mother;
And still, O Lord, to me impart
An innocent and grateful heart,
That after my great sleep I may
Awake to thy eternal day! Amen

Samuel Taylor Coleridge

YOUR FAMILY AND HOME LIFE

Tell me about your brothers and sisters. Which siblings were you really close to when you were growing up?

Did you have pets? If you did, what were they and what were their names?

Were there things that you always did together as a family?
What were those things?

What were your grandparents' names and did you visit them often?

What are your fondest memories of your grandparents?

Where did you live when you were small and in what kind of house?

Did you move a lot? Where else did you live?

What did your bedroom look like when you were growing up

Do you have any sad memories from your childhood?
Did anything bad happen to you?

How were your birthdays celebrated when you were growing up?

What was the loveliest present that you ever got for your birthday?

Can you remember the first birthday party you threw for me?

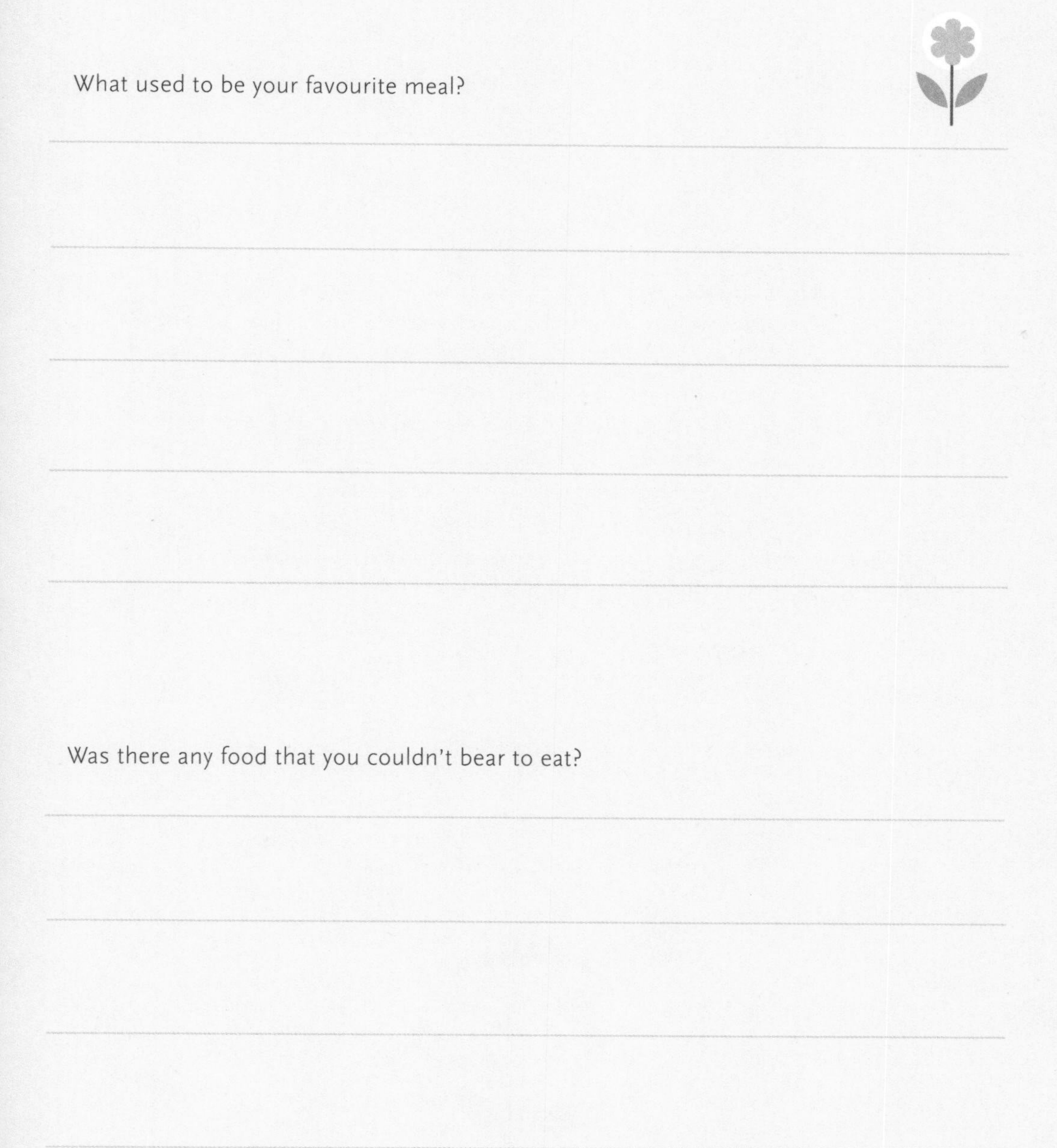

What used to be your favourite meal?

Was there any food that you couldn't bear to eat?

I remember distinctly my third birthday. The sense of my own importance surges up in me. We are having tea in the garden – in the part of the garden where, later, a hammock swings between two trees.

There is a tea table and it is covered with cakes, with my birthday cake, all sugar icing and with candles in the middle of it. Three candles. And then the exciting occurrence – a tiny red spider, so small that I can hardly see it, runs across the white cloth. And my mother says: 'It's a lucky spider, Agatha, a lucky spider for your birthday...' And then the memory fades.

AUTOBIOGRAPHY
Agatha Christie

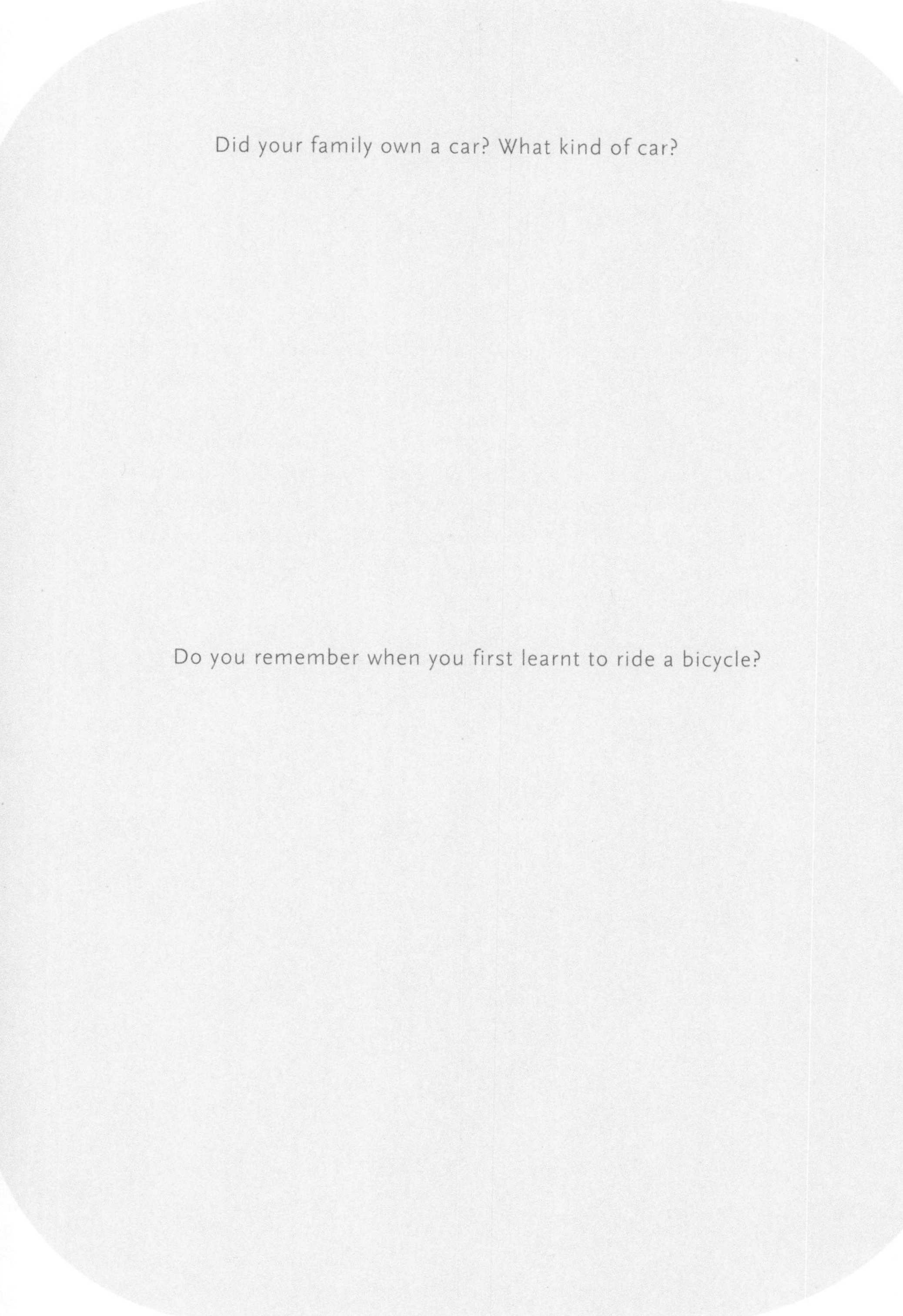

Did your family own a car? What kind of car?

Do you remember when you first learnt to ride a bicycle?

Can you tell me something about your holidays as a child?

How did you used to celebrate Christmas and New Year's Eve?

Did your family celebrate any other religious holidays?

Here's room for more memories about your family

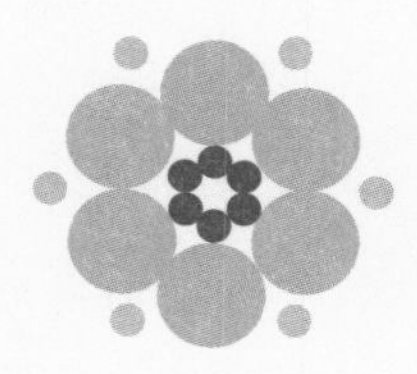

What was your primary school like?

What was your favourite subject?

And which subject did you really dislike?

Who used to be your favourite teacher at primary school?

Who were your best friends in primary school?

What did you used to do after school?

What did you want to be when you grew up?

Did you enjoy your secondary school? Did you work hard?
What sort of grades did you get?

Were you ever a prefect?

Did you wear a school uniform?
And, if so, what was it like?

Were you sporty?

Describe one moment when you laughed your head off in school

Were you ever naughty? What was the naughtiest thing you did at school?

God could not be everywhere
and therefore he made mothers
Jewish Proverb

Is there anyone you wished you had stayed in touch with?

Were you an easy-going or rebellious teenager?

What made you angry or frustrated?

What made you happy?

How did you dress when you were growing up? What was the fashion?
What was your favourite piece of clothing that would be really out of fashion today?

Which music was popular when you were growing up?

Has your taste in music changed over the years?
What music do you listen to now?

Who were the big musicians and bands when you were growing up? What was your favourite song by them?

Did you have a crush on a particular singer or band?

What books did you really love?

Did you have any films that you loved?

I was still young enough then to be sleeping with my Mother, which to me seemed life's whole purpose. We slept together in the first-floor bedroom on a flock-filled mattress in a bed of brass rods and curtains. Alone, at that time, of all the family, I was her chosen dream companion, chosen from all for her extra love; my right, so it seemed to me.

So in the ample night and the thickness of her hair I consumed my fattened sleep, drowsed and nuzzling to her warmth of flesh, blessed by her bed and safety... That darkness to me was like the fruit of sloes, heavy and ripe to the touch. It was a darkness of bliss and simple languor, when all edges seemed rounded, apt and fitting; and the presence for whom one had moaned and hungered was found not to have fled after all.

CIDER WITH ROSIE

Laurie Lee

EARLY ADULTHOOD

What did you do when you left school? Did you go to university?

Where did you live when you first left home? How old were you?
Did you live with friends?

Did you miss home?

Here is some space for more memories about this time

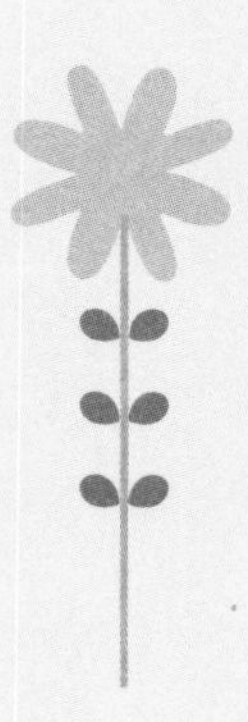

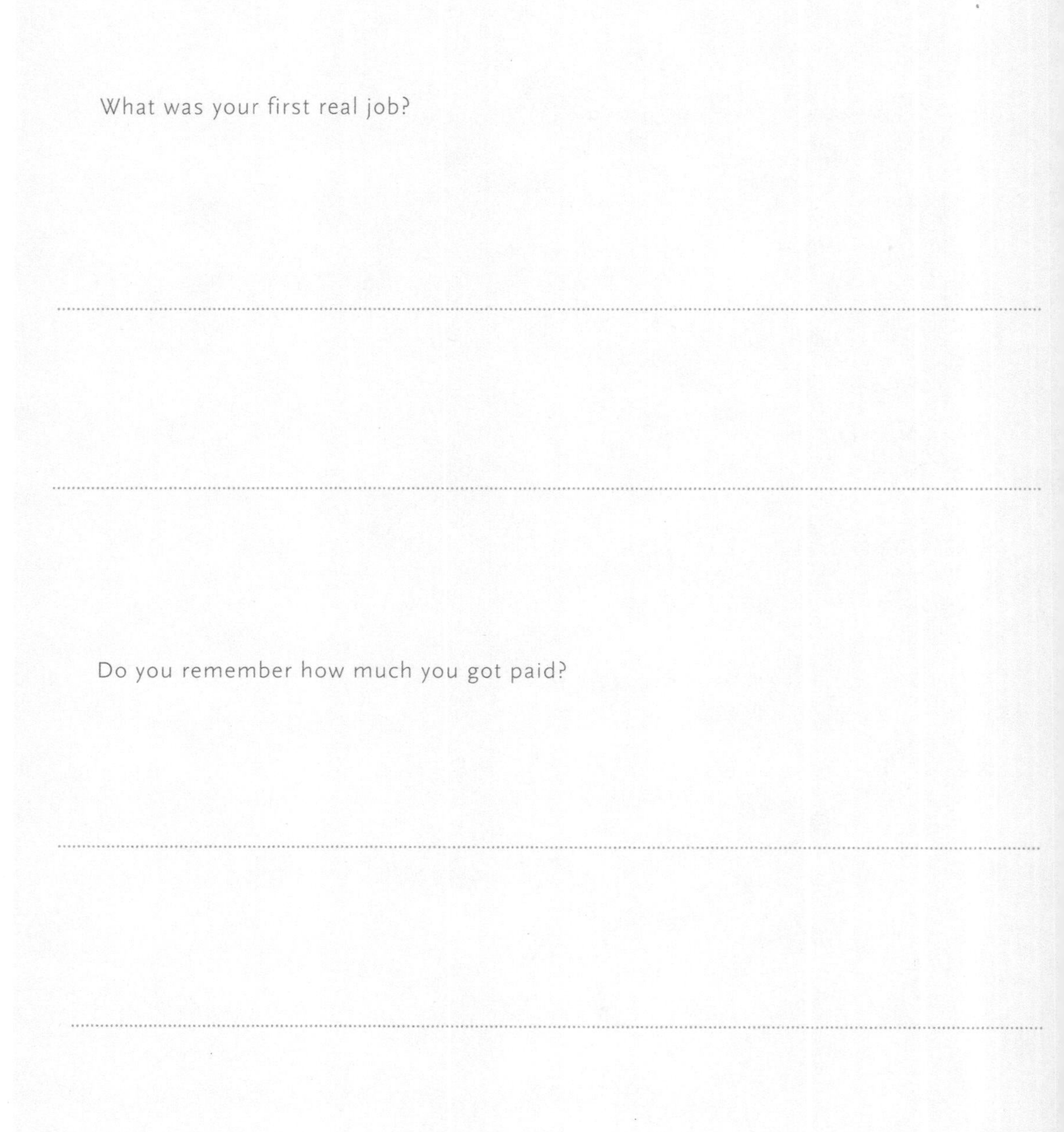

What was your first real job?

Do you remember how much you got paid?

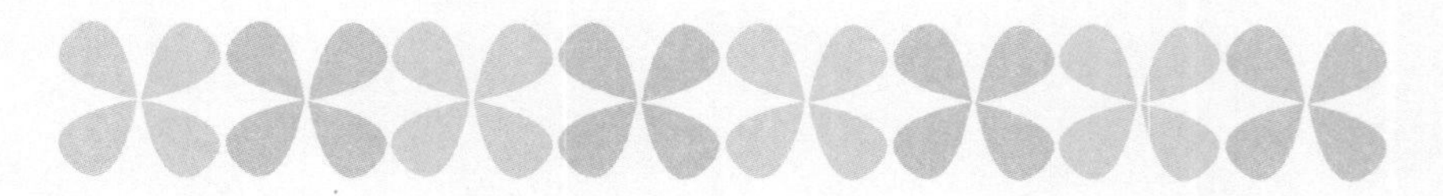

Can you remember something that you really had to save up for?

What was your biggest extravagance then?

What did you do after your first job?

Which of your jobs did you like the best?

Do you think we have a different attitude to work now?

Do you have any regrets about your career path?

What would be your career advice to me?

The heart of a mother is a deep abyss at the bottom of which you will always find forgiveness.

Honoré de Balzac

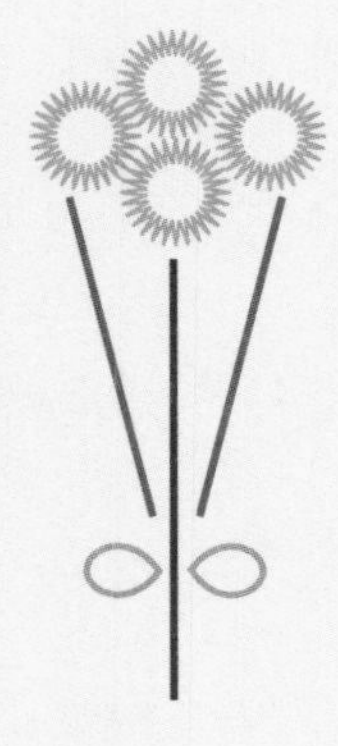

We were not coming out for another two years – it seemed an eternity, especially to Linda, who was paralysed by her longing for love, and had no lessons or work to do which could take her mind off it. In fact, she had no other interest except hunting, even the animals seemed to have lost all charm for her, and we did nothing on non-hunting days but sit about... and play endless games of patience..

We were of course both in love, but with people we had never met; Linda with the Prince of Wales, and I with a fat, red-faced, middle-aged farmer, whom I sometimes saw riding through Shenley. These loves were strong, and painfully delicious; they occupied all our thoughts, but I think we half realized that they would be superceded in time by real people...

THE PURSUIT OF LOVE

Nancy Mitford

LOVE OR SOMETHING LIKE IT...

Did you have a first crush? Who was he?

Who was your first kiss? How did you feel about it?

Who was your first real love and how did you meet?

Do you still remember what you did on the evening of your first date?

How did your parents feel about your first date?

Did you have the facts of life explained to you and by who?

Have you ever had a broken heart? How did you cope?

What is your best remedy for healing a broken heart?

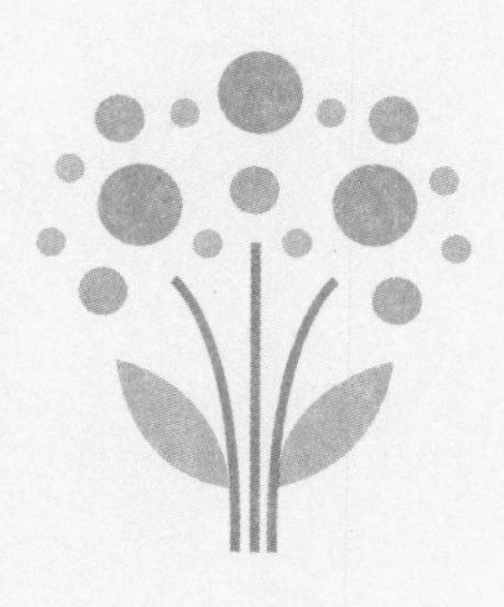

Do you think finding someone is easier now than it was when you were young?

What is the most amusing way someone has shown you that they like you?

Were you a romantic?
Did you dream of a white wedding?

How did you meet dad? Tell me about the early days of your relationship

What are your views on marriage?
Have they changed over the years and, if so, why?

What relationship advice would you give me?

What is one of the most romantic things that has ever happened to you?

FRIENDS AND FUN

Did you like to go out a lot when you were young?
Did you like going to nightclubs and parties?

What was a night out like in your twenties?
Did you have dinner with girlfriends, or did you go on lots of dates?

What was a night out like in your thirties?
Maybe you had children and were married by then – did that change things?

Do you remember when I went on my first night out, and what I was going to do?

Do you remember how you felt about it?

Did you worry if I was out late at night?

Here's room for some pictures of you having fun!

In the sheltered simplicity of the first days after a baby is born, one sees again the magical closed circle, the miraculous sense of two people existing only for each other.

Anne Morrow Lindbergh

Did you always know you wanted to have children?

When did you know you were ready to become a mother?
Or didn't it happen like that?

Was getting pregnant easy for you?

How did you find out you were pregnant and do you remember how you felt about it?

Did you get a lot of help when you were pregnant?

Did your relationship with your mother change during pregnancy?

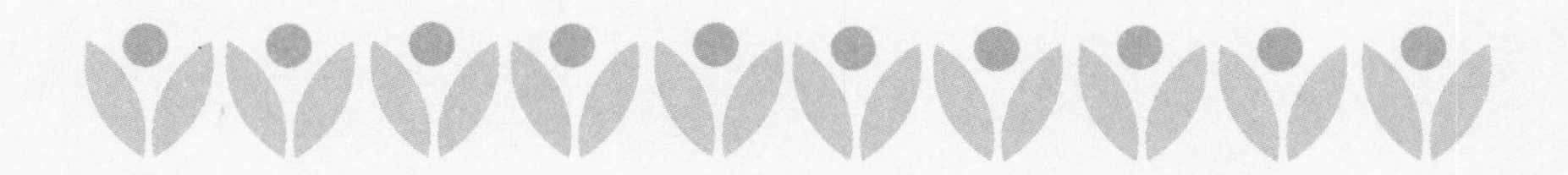

Did she tell you what it was really like to give birth?

How did your partner feel about your pregnancy?

Where did you give birth and did it go according to plan?

What were the first few weeks of being a mother like?

'Push,' said Shona, the midwife.

I pushed, the doctor pulled and Mum held on.

Then the baby was on my stomach and I was crying. She was long-limbed, dark-haired, blood-smeared and perfect. She had lips like rose-buds. I put my arms over her and I knew, suddenly and unexpectedly, that I had always been put on this earth for one reason only: to give life to this child.

'Cup of tea?' asked the midwife, propping a cup next to me on the bed.

'That'll do you good' said Mum, 'put a bit of sugar in it.'

'I hate sugar in my tea.'

THE VIEW FROM THIS END

Alexandra Fuller

Did you have set ideas about how you wanted to bring me up?
And did you stick to them or did they change?

What did you like most about raising children?

What was the hardest part?

What have you always wanted to protect your children against?

James, James
Said to his Mother,
'Mother,' he said, said he;
'You must never go down to the end of the town,
if you don't go down with me.'

'DISOBEDIENCE'

When we were very young, 1924

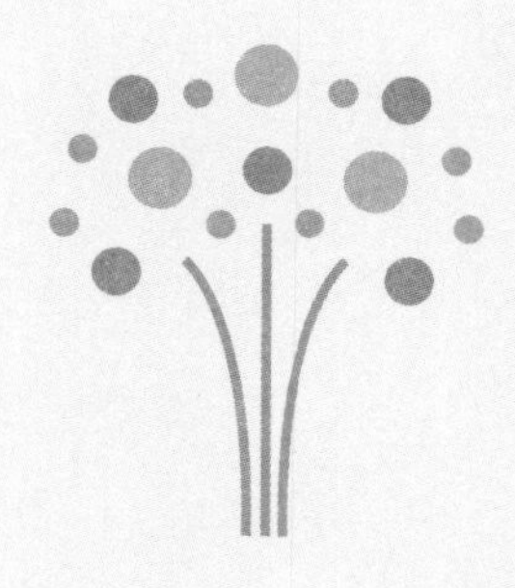

Did the way your parents raised you influence the way you raised me?
And, if so, how?

Do you think raising children nowadays is more difficult than it used to be?

What are your best bits of advice on raising children?

What changed in you when you had children?

If you had the chance to change one aspect of how you raised me, what would it be?

What have you taught me that you are most proud of?

Here's room for more memories about being pregnant and having children

MEMORIES FROM THE KITCHEN

Did you always like/dislike cooking?

What used to be my favourite food?
Was there anything I really hated but you still made me eat?

What is your favourite food?

Here's room for some of your favourite recipes

Recipes

Recipes

Recipes

Here's room for some holiday pictures

TRAVEL

Can you write down all the places you have travelled to in your life?

What is your favourite destination and why?

Do you think you are a country person or a city person?

What is your favourite type of holiday?

Can you recall one of your best holidays?

Can you recall one of your worst holidays?

Which country would you still absolutely love to visit and why?

Who and what would you take with you if you went to a desert island for a week?

What would be your eight desert island discs?
And why are they so important to you?

Motherhood brings as much joy as ever, but it still brings boredom, exhaustion, and sorrow too. Nothing else ever will make you as happy or as sad, as proud or as tired, for nothing is quite as hard as helping a person develop his own individuality especially while you struggle to keep your own.

Marguerite Kelly and Elia Parsons

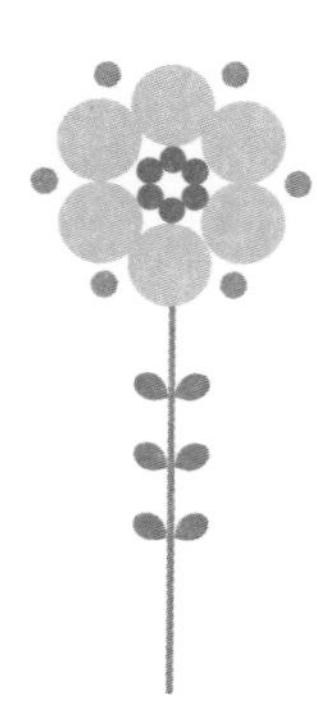

THE SERIOUS STUFF

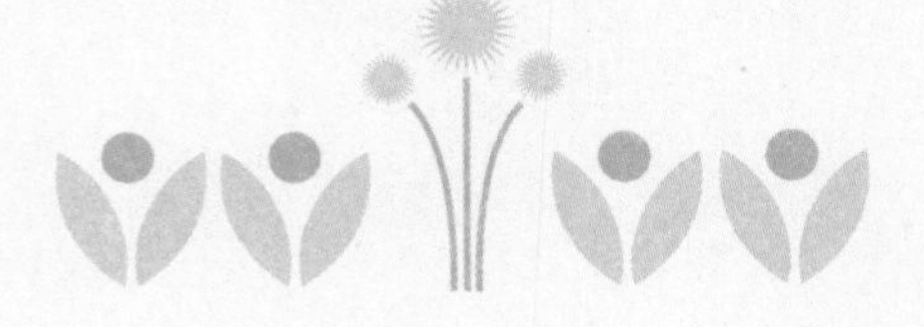

If you had a motto in life, what would it be?

What could my generation learn from yours?

What does happiness mean to you and has that changed over time?

Do you believe in miracles?

Have you changed as a person as you have grown older?

What do you think men could learn from women, and vice versa?

Do you consider yourself to be religious?

Have you known anyone who has suffered from a serious illness?
How did you cope with that?

Have there been important people in your life who have died?
How did you cope with that loss?

What is your view of death?

How would you like people to remember you after you have died?

What thoughts comfort you during difficult times?

What are your dreams at the moment?
What would you still really like to experience/do?

What would you do if you had only one month left to live?

What do you think everyone should have done or seen at least once in their life?

Here is room for any more thoughts you may have on life

All children, except one, grow up

PETER PAN

JM Barrie

Is there a smell, a sound or something else that will always remind you of a special moment in the past?

Can you tell me a dream of yours that has come true?

Do you regret certain choices you have made in your life?

What moment or event would you like to do over again if you were given the chance, and what would you do differently?

What is the best decision you have ever made in your life?

What famous person do you greatly respect and admire?
Can you tell me why?

My mother had a great deal of trouble with me,
but I think she enjoyed it

Mark Twain

What is one of your greatest achievements in life? Was it difficult to achieve?

What choices that I have made in my life are you really proud of?

All I am, or can be, I owe to my angel mother

Abraham Lincoln

What does friendship mean to you?

Who are your really great friends now?

What are the most important things that your friends have taught you?

What is the main difference between the person you used to be, and the person you are now?

Can you tell me some of your best characteristics?

What characteristics do you admire in me?

What makes you feel afraid?

What makes you cry with laughter?

If you were leader of this country for a day, what would be the first decision you would make?

What in your eyes has been one of the most significant events in your lifetime?

Tell me something that you like about getting older

What is the most difficult part of getting older?

How do you deal with the physical aspects of getting older?

What do you like about your own body?

What strikes you most when you meet someone for the first time?

What has the ability to move you deeply?

Motherhood: all love begins and ends there.

Robert Browning

I crept close to my mother's side according to my old custom, broken now a long time, and sat with my arms embracing her waist, and my little red cheek on her shoulder, and once more felt her beautiful hair drooping over me – like an angel's wing as I used to think, I recollect – and was very happy indeed.

DAVID COPPERFIELD

Charles Dickens

Write down 10 questions you would like to ask me:

Mother's Song

If snow falls on the far field
where travellers
spend the night,

I ask you, cranes,
to warm my child in your wings.

Anon (Japanese)

Every book has a last page, and this book does too.

But it also has an open ending,
because this story isn't finished yet.

First published as "*Mam vertel's!*" in Holland by Uitgeverij Het Spectrum B.V., Utrecht, 2004

First published in UK in 2008 by
Short Books
3A Exmouth House
Pine Street
London EC1R 0JH

10 9 8 7 6 5 4 3 2 1

A CIP catalogue record for this book is available from the British Library.

Designed by Georgia Vaux
Illustrations by Georgia Vaux

ISBN 978-1-906021-09-2

Printed in Italy by L.E.G.O Spa